PECULIAR PETS

Treasured Voices

Edited By Byron Tobolik

First published in Great Britain in 2021 by:

 Young**Writers**®
Est. 1991

Young Writers
Remus House
Coltsfoot Drive
Peterborough
PE2 9BF
Telephone: 01733 890066
Website: www.youngwriters.co.uk

Printed and bound in the UK by BookPrintingUK
Website: www.bookprintinguk.com
YB0458P

FOREWORD

Welcome Reader!

Are you ready to discover weird and wonderful creatures that you'd never even dreamed of?

For Young Writers' latest competition we asked primary school pupils to create a Peculiar Pet of their own invention, and then write a poem about it! They rose to the challenge magnificently and the result is this fantastic collection full of creepy critters and amazing animals!

Here at Young Writers our aim is to encourage creativity in children and to inspire a love of the written word, so it's great to get such an amazing response, with some absolutely fantastic poems. Not only have these young authors created imaginative and inventive animals, they've also crafted wonderful poems to showcase their creations and their writing ability. These poems are brimming with inspiration. The slimiest slitherers, the creepiest crawlers and furriest friends are all brought to life in these pages – you can decide for yourself which ones you'd like as a pet!

I'd like to congratulate all the young authors in this anthology, I hope this inspires them to continue with their creative writing.

★ CONTENTS ★

Alfie Virgo (10)	58
Summer Nash (9)	59
Miaya Dernie (9)	60
Bethany Clarke (10)	61
Lewis Worrall (9)	62
Amir Rahman (9)	63
Charlie Wilkinson (9)	64
Ella Tilley (9)	65
William Bourne (9)	66
Lauren Crisp (9)	67
Dominic Attwell (9)	68
Isabelle Dewey (10)	69
Imogen Forsyth-Ball (10)	70
Rosie Wyatt (9)	71
Holly Mai Preece (10)	72
Pascale Brookes (10)	73
Olivia Fitzjohn (9)	74
Zoe Tudor (10)	75
Elliot Cutler (9)	76
Bessie King (9)	77
Elise Round (10)	78
Mia Ravenhill (9)	79
Poppy Biddle (10)	80
Violet Weavers (10)	81
Cora Roncella (9)	82
Alfie Hyams (9)	83
Chloe Weaver (10)	84
Archie Holmes (10)	85
Tarlia Brookes (10)	86

Langlands Primary School, Forfar

Layla Cortese (10)	87
Rocco Bernard (10)	88
Alex Curran (10)	89
Ellie Proctor (10)	90
Eilidh Craik (9)	91

Little Heaton CE Primary School, Rhodes, Middleton

Matilda McGrath (7)	92
Emily Branchflower (9)	93
Isobelle Langton (10)	94
Maia Rogers (9)	95
Jayden Odukoya (7)	96
Daisy Dominik (9)	97
Maximus Ravenscroft (7)	98
Elliot Chambers (8)	99
Zara Yoldizska (7)	100
Adele Cerina (7)	101
Izabela Krol (7)	102
Michael Garrity (9)	103
Owen Jon Collins (10)	104
Isaac Hall (7)	105
Romi Cartmill (7)	106
Henrijs Dreimanis (9)	107
Ada Airey (7)	108
Derek Boyd (9)	109
Evelynn Jennings (9)	110

North Beckton Primary School, Beckton

Amber Suttie (10)	111

Sacred Heart Primary School, Battersea

Anujan Nirubaraj (9)	112

St David's Primary School, Plains

Igor Luc (9)	113
Nicole Paterson (9)	114
Aaron McDonald (8)	115
Erin Hughes (9)	116
Joseph Docherty (9)	117
Harris Rodgers (9)	118
Kaylee White (9)	119
Reece Rogerson (9)	120
Conlan Lane (9)	121

St Mary's Catholic Primary School, Newcastle-Under-Lyme

Ilona Dabal (9)	122
Brandon Lewis (9)	123
Vismaya Suresh (9)	124
Cobi Greenhalgh (10)	125
Jayden Laidlaw (9)	126
Jathurika Thineswaran (9)	127
Phoenix Tomlinson (9)	128
Noel Jomon (9)	129
Marcus Otter (10)	130
Jake Huxley (9)	131
Archie Bailey (9)	132
Millie Barker (9)	133
Myles Rogers (9)	134
Sulaiman Alam (9)	135

St Thomas' CE Primary School, Stockton Heath

Elizabeth Lees (11)	136
Amy Smith (10)	139
Ava Rutter (10)	140
Daniel Bruford (10)	143
Phoebe Roberts (10)	144
Kitty Rose Richards (11)	146
Chloe Porter (10)	147
Millie Garner (10)	148
George Lawton (10)	149

Swaffham Prior CE Primary School, Swaffham Prior

Willow Taw (7)	150
Luciana Verlander (8)	151
Daisy Jarvis Bently (8)	152

The Orchard School, Canterbury

Kane Ryan Barlow (10)	153

Watlington Community Primary School, Watlington

Phoebe Nicol (9)	154

Wemms Education Centre, Leatherhead

Amélie Russell (10)	155

THE POEMS

COME ON SLOW COACH

Embers

This painstakingly peculiar and rather rhetorical
poem is about a marvellously magical, incredibly
interesting, little dragon called Embers,
Embers is a young, playful dragon with a super
sense of right and wrong,
He is more curious than furious - an odd quality in
a dragon,
If he wanted to, he could fly to the clouds,
He did it once and oh, the fall! it knocked him out
for days,
Had we lost the innocent little dragon forever?
No! The dragon lived!
He fought our foes and slept with us in bed.
Embers breathed flames of a beautiful green,
As slippery as a fish, he frolicked through the fields
until night cast a veil and we retired to bed,
So long live great Embers of meadow and moor,
And mountains and the sea's shore.
The tale of Embers is happy but short,
And somewhere he still plays happily and merry
without a thought...

Elijah King (9)
Archdeacon Griffiths CIW (VA) Primary School, Llyswen

Mango The Flamango

M ango had a massive moustache

A nd a glowing witch's hat

N ow Mango's moustache grew and grew as long as a mat

G o, go, go, his favourite show is on

O n the sofa he laid down, then fell fast asleep

T he mango woke up so fluffy and puffy like a marshmallow

H e had a dream that he was running through a meadow

E nd of his amazing dream, he was a bit sad that his dream ended

F inding some food, some crisps or some cookies

L ovely fruit waiting for him on the table

A rgh! I want food now!

M ango was so mad, he had no food left

A nd I didn't go shopping, did I?

N o, why, why, why...?

G o, go, go to the sofa. He laid and fell asleep for a day

O hhh, you're so cute and fluffy.

Sorcha Lloyd (10)
Archdeacon Griffiths CIW (VA) Primary School, Llyswen

I Love My Bunny

There is a devil rabbit whose name is Lucifer,
Because he was named after the Devil.
He's really, really cute,
But he is really, really deadly,
But he has never done anything bad to me.
I really, really love him,
But he devours people's souls,
But he has got better.
Lucifer flies in the kitchen and steals the food,
And he loves to trick people,
And gives people curses.
He tries to calm down,
But he is born evil.
But he is perfect to me and I love him.

Nell (9)
Archdeacon Griffiths CIW (VA) Primary School, Llyswen

Dammon The Dancing Dog

D ancing is his power
"A nother dance," they call
M otivated by the sounds

M oving to the music
O nlookers clapping and cheering
N othing can stop him doing what he loves

T he audience like his groovy moves
H is owner gathers money in a cap
E veryone gives generously

"D ammon," they shout, "we love your groovy
moves!"
"A nother dance!" they call
N imbly he flips and turns
C ircling, twisting and jiving
I n and out of the crowds
N ose twitching and tail wagging
G iant leaps and sideward steps

D ammon loves to dance until he tires
O nlookers slowly drift away
G oodbye Dammon until another day.

Tom Jones (10)
Archdeacon Griffiths CIW (VA) Primary School, Llyswen

Bumble Buzzer

B ees buzzing all over town
U nbelievable, yes, they buzz all day long
M iss Queen is the buzziest of them all
B ees are busy all the time, *buzz!*
L ittle, they are superstars
E verything is cool, but bees are the best

B ut bees are better than cats
U nfair to not be me
Z ap, zap, zap
Z im, zap, I'm coming
E arth is nice, but I am better
R ules are simple for the bees.

Ellie Hanson (7)
Archdeacon Griffiths CIW (VA) Primary School, Llyswen

Snowy And Perry

S nowy and Perry the penguins
N ot as wild as they seem
O h, they're adorable and helpful
W ater breathing powers
Y ou should see their cute eyes

A nd
N othing and nobody else is better than Perry
D on't misjudge them

P erry and Snowy are friends forever
E ven after an argument
R unning away from predators
R unning on the snow
Y ou should see them.

Kayleigh Lewis (10)
Archdeacon Griffiths CIW (VA) Primary School, Llyswen

Fantastic Fifi The Firefly

I have a peculiar pet firefly,
Her name is Fifi and she likes to cry,
When I need to do shopping,
She suddenly starts greatly growing,
Fifi loves it when she gets ridden,
But she also likes to be hidden,
When Fifi finds things awkward,
She turns incredibly invisible and goes upward,
Fifi never gets put in a jar,
So she can fly fantastically far,
That's all I have to say,
Because she has just flown far away.

Gwennie Williams (10)
Archdeacon Griffiths CIW (VA) Primary School, Llyswen

Billy The Silly

I have a pet called Billy,
He is very silly.
He will bite you,
But he might hide in your shoe.
If you put him in his cage,
He will let out his rage.
He likes to swim,
If there is a race, he is sure to win.
He likes to sleep in bed,
With his favourite toy Ted.
He likes to eat toast,
He always eats the most.
Now he goes into his cage,
This is when he lets out his rage!

Dylan Luckhurst (10)
Archdeacon Griffiths CIW (VA) Primary School, Llyswen

Henry's Tunes

B y the edge of the deep blue sea
A playful whale can be seen!
B y the way, he loves to play the flute
Y ou could always go and listen to his tunes

W ould you go and listen?
H enry would always let you play
A ll the time he's having fun
L ong time to get to his house
E veryone knows about him and his wonderful tunes.

Ellis Hughes (10)
Archdeacon Griffiths CIW (VA) Primary School, Llyswen

The Fattest Piranha

Last week, I saw the biggest, most ferocious
piranha in the world,
It was really fast, fat and clever,
And then Alexander got fed a blue whale,
I was like it won't eat it, but it did,
Then I started laughing because it was so funny,
That I was practically crying with laughter,
And then it suddenly jumped so far out of the
water,
It made a gigantic splash that covered me with
water.

Ethan Harley (10)
Archdeacon Griffiths CIW (VA) Primary School, Llyswen

Willy The Worm

Willy the worm wriggles around,
So loud you'll hear such a sound,
He likes playing video games,
Don't take him away,
Otherwise, you'll never see him again,
His wings are very pretty,
He would love to see a city,
He likes to walk on his human-like legs,
They are a brown colour like a wooden peg,
His favourite food is lettuce,
And he is friends with a dentist.

Megan Nicholls (10)
Archdeacon Griffiths CIW (VA) Primary School, Llyswen

Remmy The Rat

Remmy is a rat,
He lives under a mat.
When he roams the streets,
He runs over people's feet.
Remmy can run over 100 miles per hour,
He lives in a massive tower.
Remmy is a fast rat,
Remmy's enemy is the neighbour's cat.
He sneaks into the shops, eating all of the cheese,
Now he has got really bad knees.
Remmy is not a scary rat,
He does not bite back.

Anna Stuart (10)
Archdeacon Griffiths CIW (VA) Primary School, Llyswen

Nugget The Chicken

My chicken can fly over the moon
Faster than a balloon.
Higher and higher,
Then he is on fire.
He comes down faster than a cheetah every time.
He lands on the tyre,
And then he goes to bed,
To rest his head.
He has some toast,
And he always has the most.
Then he boasts,
Because he had the most.
I love him so much,
I wouldn't swap him for the world.

Max Davies (11)
Archdeacon Griffiths CIW (VA) Primary School, Llyswen

D J Donkey

D J Donkey is so cool
J ee, she can fly higher than the moon

D onkey is the queen
O MG, she can light the sky
N o donkey is cooler than me
K itKats are cool, but I am better
E verything is nice, but I am better
Y ou and me make a really good team.

Menna Williams (7)
Archdeacon Griffiths CIW (VA) Primary School, Llyswen

My Dog Bolt

B ad but nice
O h, so cute
L oves his unicorn horn
T ell him off, he won't listen

T rusting, not
H appy sometimes
E ating all the time

D anger is his middle name
O h, so silly
G ood at hunting.

Owain Powell (9)
Archdeacon Griffiths CIW (VA) Primary School, Llyswen

Alwena

A lwena is a horse
L oves her field and her friends
W hen it is night-time she turns into a unicorn
E xtraordinary as can be and flies high in the sky
N ever is there a night that she does not turn into
a unicorn
A s sassy as can be.

Ruby Havard (11)
Archdeacon Griffiths CIW (VA) Primary School, Llyswen

Lazy But Cool

She likes to laze around on her cuddly carrot,
She is as colourful as a perfect parrot,
She is as gentle as a soft breeze,
She is as lazy as a piece of cheese,
She does not like to bounce around,
But she does like to sit around.

Lellia Javary (8)
Archdeacon Griffiths CIW (VA) Primary School, Llyswen

D J Dog

D J Dog discos on the moon
J iggle, juggle doggy

D *osh*, it's a party
O n the road definitely
G o! Go! Go!

Freddie Metcalfe (7)
Archdeacon Griffiths CIW (VA) Primary School, Llyswen

Fluffy

Fluffy is a dangerous, tame, furry beast,
He likes to sleep, walk and feast.
He likes to eat Shredded Wheat,
He is bright like stars in the night.

Holly Summerfield-Morgan (8)
Archdeacon Griffiths CIW (VA) Primary School, Llyswen

Eagle The Beagle

Eagle the beagle can fly sky-high,
Eagle the beagle can fly, oh, that rhymes,
Eagle the beagle can fish and fly,
Eagle the beagle can say goodbye.

Thomas Dolan (9)
Archdeacon Griffiths CIW (VA) Primary School, Llyswen

D J Dog

D J Dog is in the house
J et is in the house

D J is on the road
O n to rock them
G o, go, go!

Freddie Alderson (8)
Archdeacon Griffiths CIW (VA) Primary School, Llyswen

Chicken Bru

Hc is very funny,
And very furry,
He is adventurous,
And awesomely adorable,
He is messy and also magic,
And lovely but loud.

Elin Inseal (9)
Archdeacon Griffiths CIW (VA) Primary School, Llyswen

The Fluffy Corn

The fluffycorn likes fish and chips,
And she can also do backflips,
The fluffycorn can also climb,
And now it is her bedtime.

Evelyn Lewis (9)
Archdeacon Griffiths CIW (VA) Primary School, Llyswen

My Pet

My little, cheeky Buddy,
Fluffy, loud and grey.
He darts really quickly,
Like an arrow from a bow.

Alfie Brimble (9)

Archdeacon Griffiths CIW (VA) Primary School, Llyswen

Otter

It is clever,
It is slimy,
It has small feet.

Answer: It is an otter.

Archie Davies (8)
Archdeacon Griffiths CIW (VA) Primary School, Llyswen

Dog On A Log

The dog was sitting on a log,
He ran in the mist,
And then he tripped on the log.

Charlie Hughes (8)
Archdeacon Griffiths CIW (VA) Primary School, Llyswen

My Pet Elephant

E ach day my pet elephant stomps
L ike a giant
E ach day my pet elephant stomps, *stomp, stomp*
P erhaps he stomps because he's hungry
H e likes hopping
A nd he likes to *stomp, stomp, stomp*
N ow my neighbours have complained
T here's no chance I can keep my pet elephant.

Alfie Wheeldon (10)
Cromford CE Primary School, Cromford

I Have A Pet Whale

W ow, she has a pet whale
H eck, her house smells like fish
A whale? Where does she keep it?
L ike in her backyard!
E ww, she smells like fish!

Aimee Stone (10)
Cromford CE Primary School, Cromford

Incredible Long Neck Lu Lu

Let me tell you about my pet,
She is very clever, the cleverest you've met.
She has a cute face like a teddy bear,
She gets very nervous when people stare.
She has a snake-like neck and can see around doors,
She has big tiger feet and stomps her paws.
She has wings like an eagle and a tail like a monkey,
A big body like a giraffe which I think is funky.
I bet you won't believe me about how she looks,
You think she is only something you read about in magical books.
I promise you it's true,
My wonderful, gigantic, incredible Long Neck Lu Lu.

Poppy Fay (7)
Dame Janet Primary Academy, Ramsgate

That Fennec Fox

The fennec fox is so peculiar,
If I had one, I'd name it Zulia,
I'd watch her run and jump around,
And hunt prey without a sound,
Her ears are big and teeth are sharp,
I'd watch her hunting in the dark,
In the morning she would come,
To play in the garden and have fun,
Off to sleep, my fox would go,
To dream about the things she knows,
Night-time comes and she is awake,
There she lays with a bellyache,
Ready to hunt until her belly is full,
With meat from prey that is small,
Her name is Zulia, she is adorable.

Charli Morgan (10)
Dame Janet Primary Academy, Ramsgate

All About My Strange Apple That Is My Pet!

I'm happy and cheerful,
I'm quite full of myself.
I'm a one a day,
I'm an apple that is alive.
I make everyone happy wherever I go,
Sometimes I get lonely, so I won't go to my owner.
I'm not what you think,
I'm much more beautiful and cuter than what you think!
I'm so loyal to my owner,
I even do all of her chores!
My name is Juicy,
I'm much luckier than you think!
Now, this is the end,
Farewell, my lucky friend.

Demi Tillson (10)
Dame Janet Primary Academy, Ramsgate

Coocoo, My Peculiar Pet

Coocoo, Coocoo, that's what they said,
When I described my marvellous pet.
She may look funny,
But she is my buddy.
Chicken, giraffe, penguin, bird,
The craziest thing you've ever heard.
Not forgetting the alligator tail,
Not as big as a great blue whale.
She's got human feet, same size as my dad's,
Steals his shoes and makes him mad.
You've heard, you've pictured, but not yet met,
Here I give you Coocoo, my peculiar pet.

Phoebe Fay (11)
Dame Janet Primary Academy, Ramsgate

My Cool Cat

My cool cat is as cool as a new hat,
It hisses like a snake,
When you make a cool cake,
When you're mowing the grass,
It looks like glass,
He likes you stroking it,
He doesn't like you poking it,
It's mean to strangers, especially gamers,
If he meets someone he likes, he's sweet,
Like the candy you eat,
Its fur is black like the night sky,
Don't ask me why,
Don't look at the sky,
But the cat has black fur.

Majid Jabar (9)
Dame Janet Primary Academy, Ramsgate

Alice The Hamster

She was a cute, fluffy ball,
She ran through the hall.
She was a cute, little hamster,
She loved Manchester.
Her fur was beige,
She chewed her cage.
She was lucky to be born,
She also loved corn.
She was a nice little girl,
Her eyes were shiny like a pearl.
She put food in her cheeks,
She kept it for weeks.
She gave us a fright,
When she escaped her cage every night.
We loved Alice very much.

Takuto Humphreys (7)
Dame Janet Primary Academy, Ramsgate

Extraordinary Geoffery

His incredible soft fur,
Puts every pet aside,
His beige fur is sweet,
He'd win against birds that go:
Tweet! Tweet!
Without Geoff,
I'm dead beat,
I cry at the thought,
Of him being meat.
It was sad to see him go,
But, he's out of his pain and,
He's in for glory, in clouds, snow...

Hannah Lawrence (11)
Dame Janet Primary Academy, Ramsgate

Why I Love Lampard

Lampard came indoors one day,
And hid himself away.
He hid behind the curtain,
His tail would show for certain.
When Daisy came in,
He started to spin,
And he chased her out,
And we stood and laughed and fell about.
Then he ran into the garden chasing rats and mice,
That's why I love him, he's so very nice.

Brooke Brown (7)
Dame Janet Primary Academy, Ramsgate

My Owl

My peculiar owl prefers day to night,
Catching her prey during her daily flight.
She spreads out her wings covered in speckles of
gold,
And sees the world's secrets begin to unfold.

When morning comes and the sun shines bright,
My owl starts to wake up from her lazy night.
Then by lunchtime, she's ready to fly,
And spreads out her wings and zooms through the
sky.

She lands in the mountains where the eagles loom,
And sings them a song that reminds them of
home.
When the song's finished, the eagles all clap,
Then my owl has to go, but she's bound to be
back.

Soon she travels to the Brittany coast,
Where she sings to some puffins who enjoy it the
most.

Her songs are amazing with a catchy tune,
And she sang so loudly you could hear it from the moon.

As day turns to dusk, her voice becomes sore,
So she makes honey and lemon, before making some more.
Then when it's bedtime, she ends her day,
By humming her songs as she scribbles away.

Ellie Lonergan (9)
EDS Writers' Club, Crowthorne

Crazy Cinders

C razy Cinders acts quite cool

I dle when she knows she is going on a wet walk

N aughty nuisance when she zooms up and down our hall

D etermined to catch our other dogs

E ats pretty, pointy feathers

R uns rapidly because she wants to lie in front of the fire first

S illy at the beach when she finds a seagull feather and runs really fast around the beach with it in her mouth.

Max Vipurs (10)

Gigha Primary School, Isle Of Gigha

The Cheviot-Cross

C razy Cheviot Buster
H eadbutts hard
E xcellent when he follows me
V ast diet of milk straight from the cow
I ncredible in size and he lives
O utdoors and he loves it, also, he is
T errific because he is the bee's knees.

Mark Dennis (9)
Gigha Primary School, Isle Of Gigha

My Peculiar, Pink Pet Panda

I have a little secret that no one must know,
It's small and fuzzy and it attacks my toes.
It lives in my bathtub submerged in water,
It's the size of my dog, just a little bit shorter.

You may have guessed what it is already,
It's kind of like my real-life teddy.
A small, pink panda that would make you blush,
But if she's sleeping, you may want to shush.

For if you wake her, you won't make a friend,
She's small but frightening and will make your hair
stand on end!
Don't worry, she won't attack you without warning,
But push her too far and you won't wake up the
next morning!

Her name is Fluffy,
And her cheeks are puffy.
She's very good and won't go and walk,
But she'll keep an eye out and listen to you talk.

She knows how to not get caught,
For that is all that she has been taught.
You may wonder how I keep such a pet,
For I wasn't the reason that we met.

It was a summer's day and very late,
And I was out wandering in the woods with my mate.
Suddenly, my mate ran away, leaving me confused,
I looked up into the tree and saw a very pink panda looking amused.

It jumped out the tree and gripped on my leg,
As small and as stern as a bright pink peg.
Please do not tell anyone,
Or I will send her to haunt you until you're twenty-one.

Holly Jones (10)
Holy Trinity School, Kidderminster

Jaxson's Story

I have a dinosaur called Jaxson,
He likes to go for a hot chocolate and sponge
cake,
(Even though he does not have any eyes or teeth).

He is pink, fluffy and he has a big nose,
No tail and twelve arms!
Because he has no eyes,
He is always bumping into things and people.

When he was younger,
He was an amazing goalkeeper,
But he got kicked out of his football team,
Because when he got too excited,
He breathed out fire,
(He was also fat and covered up the goal).

One day, the circus came to town,
And Jaxson went to watch, well, listen,
Jaxson was really interested,
And decided to sign up.
Jaxson got picked!
He ended up becoming an acrobat,

Walking on a rope on his twelve hands,
Breathing out fire and showing off his muscles.
I bet the team want to get him back now...

Jude James Foster (10)
Holy Trinity School, Kidderminster

My Very Peculiar Fred

My alien is called Fred,
He lives under my bed,
He is very red,
When my friend met him, she said,
"What a peculiar head!"

Fred is my very peculiar pet,
He is the kindest thing you've ever met,
He's one of a kind, not part of a set,
He bemuses the vet and makes her fret.
What a very peculiar pet.

He likes to come with me to after school clubs,
He even likes to go to pubs,
I give great big tummy rubs,
Right after he has finished his grubs.

Grubs are his favourite food,
Big, fat and round, I don't mean to be rude,
It's just this type of grub puts him in his best mood.

Fred really is a peculiar pet,
Without him, I think I would fret,

Our forever friendship is firmly set,
For me and Fred, my peculiar pet.

Phoebe Oldnall (10)
Holy Trinity School, Kidderminster

Odd Dog

I own quite an odd animal that I call my pet,
There's something about him that people don't get.
Sure, he's odd, but he's still my dog,
I saw him in the shop being picked on by a collie,
I bought him from a lady who calls herself Miss Polly.
He's got a fluffy tail - like most huskies do,
And lovely round eyes; both mystical blue.
His ears are placed on the top of his head,
And like his tail, they're both blood-red.
His ears are a bit like a bunny's,
And when they twitch, it is rather funny.
To add to that, instead of trotting,
This husky much prefers hopping.
I own quite an odd animal that I call my pet,
There's something about him that people don't get.
But I love Chaos; sure, he's odd,
But he's still my dog.

Ruby Jones (10)
Holy Trinity School, Kidderminster

The Mysterious Snake Monster

It's long and hairy, not short and fat,
It slithers, it slides like a big, fat cat.

Its face is human, with big afro hair,
It looks like my sister with a happy stare.

The body is long, it goes on forever,
Sliding through the bushes thinking it's clever.

The body is strange with colourful fur,
Guinea pig hair is what keeps her warm.
Rain and wind and through all the storms.

My unusual friend lives in a strange place,
It's dark and cold which could make your blood race.

She's lonely and quiet and only comes out at night,
She's scary but kind and will give you a fright.
Did I mention she's allergic to light?

Blaine O'Sullivan (9)
Holy Trinity School, Kidderminster

My Best Friend

M y best friend is a moonlight angel pup
O n Thursdays, we watch a movie
O n Fridays, she goes home
N o one can beat her
L ittle Pippin is so cute
I miss you, bestie
G ive her a treat, she isn't bad
H eaven is her home
T he sassiness she produces is hysterical

A nd the ditziness is too
N ow I have to say goodbye
G o on little pup, I'll be fine
E xtraordinary how I miss her so
L ove you Pippin, so go

P up, please come back.

Rosalie Parsons (9)
Holy Trinity School, Kidderminster

Furry, Strange Pets On The Loose!

They're furry, they're small,
Some big and many more!
Have you seen my friend Peggie?
Come on, let's explore!
Where could he be...?
Oh wait, maybe behind this tree!
Awh... still no sign of Peggie.
Maybe here, maybe there,
Come on, let's look everywhere!
Could he be in a zoo?
Gasp! There you are Peggie,
Ew, look at you...
Finally, you're all clean,
Let's have a bedtime read!
Doodle Mum will tuck you into bed,
Just sip up your warm milk,
And goodnight, off to bed!

Jalen Macnamara-Sharma (10)
Holy Trinity School, Kidderminster

The Flying Hamster

F lying hamster won't go to bed
L ately, I am tired
Y ou stop now
"I don't want it anymore," I say
N ow, let's take it away
G reat

H ow about today
A fter we play?
"M aybe," I say, "don't take it away."
"S orry, we can't take it away."
"T ake it away," I say
"E r, matey, not today."
"R un," I say.

Grace Tilley (9)
Holy Trinity School, Kidderminster

Siberia

My name is Siberia,
And I'm very peculiar.
I have a telepathic mind,
It helps me with food I want to find.
Occasionally, I take a swim,
But don't like my owner going to the gym.
I am 1/3 rabbit, 1/3 dog, 1/3 Savannah cat,
What do you think about that?
I have long, pink bunny ears, a spotted cat's tail,
And a medium-sized dog body which is very, very
pale.
I am gentle not ferocious, incredibly furry and
agile,
But my feelings can be very extraordinary and
fragile.

Seren Turley (10)
Holy Trinity School, Kidderminster

Teddy

The day you wagged into my life,
We bonded from the start.
I called you Teddy,
Because you are big and feathery.
Your rainbow feathers and claws,
Make you extraordinary.
My messy Teddy leaves his colourful feathers,
All over my sofa made of leather.
As he considers it to be,
His favourite place to be clever.
Whenever he makes his toys come alive,
With his magical powers.
No matter what Teddy does,
He always brings happiness into my life.

Leila Miah (10)
Holy Trinity School, Kidderminster

Penny!

Penny is a very peculiar pet
We found her in a net
She is a dragon crossed with a furry dog
And boy, when she eats, she eats like a hog
She looks like a big, ferocious dragon
But she is cute and very lazy, so drives around in a wagon
She is very agile and can fly very high
She will try, but can never reach the sky
She breathes fire to help us cook tea
Until she runs off to chase a bee
Penny is a peculiar pet
But I haven't met a better pet yet.

Matthew Lyons (9)
Holy Trinity School, Kidderminster

My Peculiar Pet

On a normal planet,
Most people would have normal pets,
Lots of normal equals boring,
That's why we have a peculiar planet,
On this peculiar planet,
Most people have peculiar pets,
I am one of those people.

My peculiar pet is a tortoise,
It's a six-foot high, speedy tortoise,
My tortoise refuses to eat anything except steak,
His name is Gerald.

Gerald is very expensive,
But he's worth it,
I love Gerald.

Oskar Harper (9)
Holy Trinity School, Kidderminster

My Bunny

My bunny who is called Daisy,
Is a little bit lazy,
She is so sassy,
But she is not fussy,
Daisy is marvellous,
But never dangerous,
She likes carrots,
But hates parrots,
She is not colourful,
But she is very lovable,
I love my bunny,
Because she is so funny,
Daisy is not grumpy,
But can be jumpy,
She doesn't like the sun,
But loves to run,
She is my little hun,
And I am her mum.

Jasmine Kunya (10)
Holy Trinity School, Kidderminster

My Astro Zebra

My astro zebra wants to go to Pluto,
So can you help him with his mission,
And make his dream come true?
He's creating a rocket ship,
He sat in his den to make a gem,
As the heart of all of them.
He's finally done, it's time to say goodbye,
As we all watch him fly into the midnight sky.
He came back with a smile on his face,
But he looked a mess,
And will always be a buddy,
To Pluto and be by my side.

Alfie Virgo (10)
Holy Trinity School, Kidderminster

Clever Crookshanks

Crookshanks is a ginger cat,
She likes to curl up on her mat,
She has bright green eyes,
She is very wise,
Crookshanks can cook, clean, read and write,
She would never ever hiss or bite.

Crookshanks likes to cook fish,
When she's finished, she likes to clean her dish,
She likes to read her favourite book,
Clever Crookshanks likes to wear sunglasses,
At 10 o'clock, she will go to her cooking classes.

Summer Nash (9)
Holy Trinity School, Kidderminster

The Rapping Koala

I once saw a rapping koala
Coming down my street
Then I thought, *who is he?*
In his purple T-shirt and his cool sunglasses
And also his lightning bolt microphone
He started rapping
People came out
Cheered out loud
Told me to come out
I said, "No."
Then he made me and I said, "Yo!"
Then he had to go, so I said, "Bye."
Now I'm a poet and don't you know it.

Miaya Dernie (9)
Holy Trinity School, Kidderminster

Sassy Cat

Something's turned up at my front door,
And has been bossing us around until dawn!
She's a cat, she said her name's Pixie,
She wears a red glittery dress and black shades,
Instead of saying hi, she says hey.
She's got black high heels,
I don't know how she walks in them,
Oh, and she comes from a town called Sassentem.
Moving on, she's been here for days!
And she's left us all in a daze.

Bethany Clarke (10)
Holy Trinity School, Kidderminster

The Epic Tale Of Super Dog

S mart as ever!

U p-to-date with all the fashion

P E was his favourite lesson in school

E nd of the day, when Night Cat comes

R eading his book, Super Dog gets that villain Night Cat

"D on't, oh, argh! Why, Super Dog? I was going to rob that bank," said Night Cat

O h my, oh my, Super Dog saved the day

G ood day, good day, Super Dog's saved us all.

Lewis Worrall (9)

Holy Trinity School, Kidderminster

The Kind Dragon

D reaming of a world made out of sweets

R eminding myself to give out food to the homeless

A nd eventually helping everyone in the world

G oing home to eat my lunch being happy

O ut of nowhere, I saw a homeless man and helped

N ever do bad to anyone that doesn't have a lot because you don't know what they're going through. Every day, try and help people like I did.

Amir Rahman (9)
Holy Trinity School, Kidderminster

My Magnificent Murtle

M y murtle is small but strange
Y et to learn to be like his parents

M urtles don't get bigger the older they get
U nlike other murtles, mine can talk
R hyming all of the time
T elling terrible jokes thinking they are funny
L aughing together, we have lots of fun
E veryone should have a murtle!

Charlie Wilkinson (9)
Holy Trinity School, Kidderminster

The Dog With A Fish Body

My dog Sunny is very funny,
His body is like a fish, scaly and shiny,
But his face is cute, soft and fluffy,
He swims all day and barks all night,
Giving the neighbours such a fright,
His favourite food is chocolate biscuits,
And he likes to watch cricket,
I love my pet, he is very unusual,
I wouldn't change him for anything.

Ella Tilley (9)
Holy Trinity School, Kidderminster

Speaking Sid

S eal is his form
P eculiar he is!
E ating a fish
A ny will do
K ing of the sea
I n his eyes at least!
N ight is for rest
G ood morning is the best

S peaking he can do
I n a language not known to his friends
D efinitely, definitely a peculiar pet.

William Bourne (9)
Holy Trinity School, Kidderminster

The Wonderful Octocat

The other day, the octocat was playing,
Whilst the others were thinking.
In the dark, she finds a new friend,
Next, she was playing with the new friend,
In the darkness.
Deep down it is clever, but also messy.
The cute and clawed octocat was also colourful.
Loves to fight in the night,
The fighting was all night at midnight.

Lauren Crisp (9)
Holy Trinity School, Kidderminster

My Pupycatcorn

P owerful
U pbeat
P igs, he is like a pig
Y oung, he's eight
C andy, he loves candy
A dorable
T idy, I think not
C heeky
O rdinary, seriously, he's not ordinary
R olls around in mud
N oisy, not just noisy, incredibly noisy.

Dominic Attwell (9)
Holy Trinity School, Kidderminster

My Furry Friend Fluffy

Fluffy is half dragon and half rabbit,
She sees a biscuit, she has to grab it,
She loves to play with her bat and ball,
But if she is tired, she will always fall.
Fluffy loves to go on walks,
But it is peculiar because she always talks,
Her scales on her back always move,
And occasionally she loves to groove.

Isabelle Dewey (10)
Holy Trinity School, Kidderminster

The Cerbil

Am I cat,
Sitting on a mat?
Or am I a dog,
Lying next to Aragog?
Am I a frog,
Leaping on a log?
No, I'm purr-fect, scuttling around,
I am a cerbil the size of a small mound,
I am half cat, half gerbil,
I'm the cutest little furball.
I'm one of a kind,
I will blow your mind.

Imogen Forsyth-Ball (10)
Holy Trinity School, Kidderminster

Dorothy

My peculiar pet is Dorothy,
She lives in the big, blue pool.
She's really long and so spotty,
People act like she doesn't exist.
Her eyes are big, her neck is long,
And her tail is so scaly.
She gets me wet when she splashes me,
And makes me laugh so much, I want to pee.

Rosie Wyatt (9)
Holy Trinity School, Kidderminster

Frenchie

Louis,
I'm not a pig,
I'm not a pug,
I haven't been here for years,
I've only been here for months,
People call me cute,
But I can't keep myself on mute,
A tilt of the head,
From something you said,
When I get hyper,
I get told to go to bed.

Holly Mai Preece (10)
Holy Trinity School, Kidderminster

Gilles The Gecko

G reedy

I s little

L ucky

L ikes to eat me

E ats worms

S assy

T akes her time

H appy

E vil

G ood

E xtra

C ute

K ing of the castle

O ver the top.

Pascale Brookes (10)
Holy Trinity School, Kidderminster

Melanie The Peculiar Cat

M ischievous little lady
E legant like a diva
L ively - always jumps around!
A gile - always lands on her feet
N eeding attention constantly
I ndependent, strong, sassy, needs no one
E loquent chatterbox.

Olivia Fitzjohn (9)
Holy Trinity School, Kidderminster

Tweet, Tweet

Tweet, tweet, tweet in the air,
Flying high in the sky.
When he lands in his cage,
He eats all the seeds.
What a joyful sight I see,
As he tweets peacefully.
When he lands on my head,
He cuddles up like he's in his nest.

Zoe Tudor (10)
Holy Trinity School, Kidderminster

My Mythical Creature

M ix of Medusa and a minotaur
I t is dangerous
N o one but me meets it on the moor
U mm... I don't invite it to Christmas!
S am tried to catch it in a net
A nd he failed because he is a marvellous pet.

Elliot Cutler (9)
Holy Trinity School, Kidderminster

Garry The Human Giraffe!

Do you have a pet giraffe?
Well, I have and I gave him a tie,
Now he thinks he's a human,
I guess Garry is,
He goes to work and always wobbles,
Garry is a clown when he goes to the park,
But I love him with all my heart.

Bessie King (9)
Holy Trinity School, Kidderminster

Foxoroo

F antastic foxoroo

O ver energetic

'X traordinarily messy

O rdinarily cute

R anking of 1-10 stars

O nce in a lifetime chance to get to see a foxoroo

O rder now at shop.com.

Elise Round (10)

Holy Trinity School, Kidderminster

Dangerous Dan

D angerous

A ngry

N aughty

G rumpy

E xtraordinary

R otten

O bdurate

U gly

S assy

D astardly

A crid

N ot Nice.

Mia Ravenhill (9)

Holy Trinity School, Kidderminster

The Moody Mouse

I think mice are very gentle,
Their tails are long and skinny,
Their faces are small and rather messy,
Their ears are adorable,
They run around the house while you're sleeping at night,
That is why mice are nice.

Poppy Biddle (10)
Holy Trinity School, Kidderminster

Jeremey

J okester

E asy to fool

R aces everywhere

E ven round the pool

M y best friend he is

E ats all the veg like a good Jeremey

Y ay! He likes his drinks to fizz.

Violet Weavers (10)
Holy Trinity School, Kidderminster

My Pet Golden Pegasus

I have a golden pegasus
She's the best pegasus around
Her name is Liria
She eats from the ground
She has a golden horn
As gold as a crown
When she wants to fly
She kicks up off the ground.

Cora Roncella (9)
Holy Trinity School, Kidderminster

Waffle And Me

Waffle can read,
And he has a very long lead.
He can walk and talk,
Whilst eating dinner with a fork.
He flies in a car very low,
Whilst making pizza dough.
He can do everything you need to know.

Alfie Hyams (9)
Holy Trinity School, Kidderminster

My Old Octag!

O ld Octag is fun to play with
C lever enough to teach
T all like the Empire State Building
A ngry sometimes, but I can calm him down
G rumpy when it's bedtime, like me.

Chloe Weaver (10)
Holy Trinity School, Kidderminster

Rockin' Scout

Scout was mad and she had sunglasses,
She gave out some nasty gases,
She played the guitar,
But never got very far,
She wrecked everything apart from the car,
Because that was what took her far.

Archie Holmes (10)
Holy Trinity School, Kidderminster

Marty

M oody

A ttention-seeking

R are

T imid

Y oung.

Tarlia Brookes (10)

Holy Trinity School, Kidderminster

Brilliant Bertie

Brilliant Bertie is lots of fun,
He can dance all day in the sun,
Brilliant Bertie can fly up high,
He soars like an aeroplane in the sky,
Bertie can talk and he can sing,
Did I mention he's wearing a ring?
He says, "G'day mate."
Bertie loves fish bait!
Brilliant Bertie is wild, crazy, clever too,
He likes to scare people and shout, "Boo!"
He's gentle and cute, I love him so much!
He sometimes likes to sleep in a hutch,
When we go swimming, he talks and breathes
underwater,
Last but not least, he doesn't like seeing a lamb
being taken to the slaughter.

Layla Cortese (10)
Langlands Primary School, Forfar

Dumbo Dog

I met a dog,
In a log,
He's black and white,
He flies at night,
He's naughty and wild,
He likes spicy food, not mild,
He plays darts,
And is very smart,
He's called Dumbo Dog!
He's called Dumbo Dog!
He has ears like Dumbo,
And wears a JoJo bow,
He loves games,
But not those that are lame.

Rocco Bernard (10)
Langlands Primary School, Forfar

Fleg The Dog

F   urry and fabulous
L   ovely, also lazy
E   xtraordinary
G   rumpy as well as gentle

T   alented and tamed
H   opeful, also helpful
E   ager as well as excited

D   elightful and indescribable
O   ld as well as obese
G   orgeous, also gigantic.

Alex Curran (10)
Langlands Primary School, Forfar

The Sporty Dog

I once had a dog who sneaked out at night,
He seemed so bright,
I followed him out,
To find he was skateboarding about!
The best skater I have seen!
I was jealous to see,
My dog was better than me!
He came home for tea,
And finally said to me,
No need to say,
Just scream, "Hooray!"

Ellie Proctor (10)
Langlands Primary School, Forfar

Cool Cody

A limerick

There is a cool dog called Cody,
Who loves to eat baloney,
He loves to backflip,
Whilst watching Netflix,
And eating macaroni.

Eilidh Craik (9)
Langlands Primary School, Forfar

The Giraffe Who Can Climb Mountains

Bananas are her favourite food in the world,
If she hears me peel the banana,
She will run in the kitchen.

Even when she rides some jewellery every night,
She will bring a banana with her on the ride.

Teething on her teeth,
Struggling with eating, struggling with sleeping.

Having some walking time on the mountains,
Bring your babies.

Eating more food,
She brings some strawberries this time.
She gobbles them all up.

Nana's knitting some jumpers,
For my children and grandchildren.

Yippee! It's the summer holiday,
I ran and packed my bag for the holiday.

Matilda McGrath (7)
Little Heaton CE Primary School, Rhodes, Middleton

The Flying Cat Dog

F ood is fleas, bugs and bees

L ives in a brown and black shed on a green field

Y ou can see it when you walk past it and it will become your friend

I ts skin colour is pink and purple

N o touching or it will want to be your friend, okay

G o there and you can see it fly fast in the air

C an you see it yet?

A n inventor's cute and adorable cat dog

T o go there you don't need to pay

D o go there please, it means a lot

O n your way, you should see a road and a shed

G o there and at the end, we will give you £1,000 pounds.

Emily Branchflower (9)
Little Heaton CE Primary School, Rhodes, Middleton

Oliver The Owl

O liver is an adventurous owl

L ooks mad because he scowls

I f you trust me though, you can come see

V arious missions to complete

E ven though they may be hard

R equested for more missions because we have done them all in the yard

T he perfect team is right here

H elping everyone on the pier

E ven at Christmas, we don't get a day off if one has a cough

O rganisation is us, we can even do each other's jobs

W ill you join us and do more missions?

L ooks like we have a new friend!

Isobelle Langton (10)
Little Heaton CE Primary School, Rhodes, Middleton

Elegant Elephantguin

Oh, the elegant elephantguin,
Small, sassy and very fancy.
Here we go to the beach today,
Whoosh! Boom!
Off to the sea she goes,
Wearing her little tutu,
Oh, how cute, oh, how cute this elephantguin is,
But just wait till you know Elegant Elephantguin,
Small, sassy and very fancy,
Bash! Zoom!
Off to the ice cream shop she goes,
Laughing, waddling and making elephant sounds,
Oh, how cute, Oh, how cute this little elephantguin is,
But just wait till you know Elegant Elephantguin,
Small, sassy and very fancy.

Maia Rogers (9)
Little Heaton CE Primary School, Rhodes, Middleton

Magic Enchantment

D arts, he darts, he is very fast and faster than the wind

R oar! He roars like thunder, very hard

A nd his tail is like spiky leather

H is three heads spit water and hot fire

I think he is the best forever

S eeing him will give you a scare

I think you will be jealous, but don't be

R oar! His roar has a sonic boom

E nchanted power is everywhere

L et it be free forever

S uspicious, he is very suspicious

P eople run as fast as you can.

Jayden Odukoya (7)
Little Heaton CE Primary School, Rhodes, Middleton

The Unisore Rhyme

I love my little unisore,
He's sassy, messy, cute and small.
He always plays with his little ball,
And he named the ball Uncle Paul.
The day I got my abominable pet,
He trapped himself in a fishing net.
When I got him from the tangled mess,
He smelt like the rubbish dump,
Where homeless people eat their fries.
My unisore is old now,
And he doesn't have too long to live,
But hopefully he survives,
So we can do the jive.

Daisy Dominik (9)
Little Heaton CE Primary School, Rhodes, Middleton

Meet Montasouros

M ontasouros is coming
O n his way to my flying house
N ow off we go, flying really fast
T o the zoo that is magic
A nd now we're here running around
S o now we're going to his place
O n the chocolate river
U h oh! Are you listening to him roar?
R *oar!*
O n the way home, I'm sleepy
S o now we're chilling in my bed, snoring.

Maximus Ravenscroft (7)
Little Heaton CE Primary School, Rhodes, Middleton

World Explorer

S corider is my pet

C arries me on his back

O riginally he was a spider, but got bitten by a scorpion

R iding him is exciting

I go to exotic places with him

D iving under the extremely ginormous sea

E xploring, swimming, climbing and scuttling

R oaming the world on the back of Scorider is the best. The back of Scorider is the best that can be.

Elliot Chambers (8)

Little Heaton CE Primary School, Rhodes, Middleton

The Cat Who Can Do TikTok

A pples, if she eats too many apples, she will still do TikTok

D og, a cute dog in her bedroom

D octor, a very cute doctor she sees every time she breaks her leg

I gloo, if she goes to the South Pole, the penguins are so cute

S o her mum said, "Do not do TikTok."

O ranges are her favourite fruit

N ick, her friend, keeps her safe.

Zara Yoldizska (7)
Little Heaton CE Primary School, Rhodes, Middleton

Space Candyland Adventure

H ound Dog is my magical pet
O ver Jupiter, we flew to Space Candyland
U nder cotton candies, we flew together
N ow we are exploring strawberry muffins
D ogs are cheering us to fly even faster

D ogs are eating chocolate now
O w, now we go back to Earth
G oodbye, Space Candyland.

Adele Cerina (7)
Little Heaton CE Primary School, Rhodes, Middleton

Transcat On The Run

T ranscat is my peculiar pet
R unning to his friends in Differland
A way he runs in a flash through the slimy green puddles
N o one can ever catch him
S eeing everything in his land
C atching the smooth, soft apples
A t Differland, everyone likes him
T ime for bed, so he runs home.

Izabela Krol (7)

Little Heaton CE Primary School, Rhodes, Middleton

Lost Teddy

We are on a beach,
With nobody else,
He is going to get ice cream in a van,
He's eating an elf!
We are now in bed,
And nobody is here,
Because we are in a shed,
Drinking beer!
Flying up to space,
Going to Mars,
Going over to a hole,
Because he lost his teddy.
So now we are asleep,
Nun-night.

Michael Garrity (9)
Little Heaton CE Primary School, Rhodes, Middleton

My Friend Cat-O-Pilla

Hello, my friend Cat-O-Pilla
His favourite ice cream is vanilla
He is super strong
And he's super long
He likes to sit on flowers
But he wishes he had superpowers
He likes to say, "Yeet!"
He likes to eat meat
Hello, my friend Cat-O-Pilla
You're my best friend.

Owen Jon Collins (10)
Little Heaton CE Primary School, Rhodes, Middleton

Robocat

R obocat is my pet
O nly robots are allowed in space
B iting people who break the rules
O beying his masters who created him
C laws are made from extremely cold metal
A nd his eyes are like Thanos' gauntlet
T hat can snap people out of existence.

Isaac Hall (7)
Little Heaton CE Primary School, Rhodes, Middleton

Dragon Land

B ella is my amazing, incredible, peculiar pet
E veryone is seeing Bella eat yummy, tasty ice cream
L ong green grass growing on the concrete outside
L oads of black, scary lava coming down
A lot of hot, scary lava has been turned to coal from an extremely bad flood.

Romi Cartmill (7)
Little Heaton CE Primary School, Rhodes, Middleton

The Inventor Of Machines You Never Knew You Needed!

My pet is a shape-shifter cat,
Inventing is what he is good at.

Sometimes he turns into an octopus,
Then you might hear him cuss.

Once he came to school,
The teacher no longer ruled!

The crazy cat once made,
A potion of exploding Gatorade.

Henrijs Dreimanis (9)
Little Heaton CE Primary School, Rhodes, Middleton

My Flying Dog

N ella is my peculiar pet

E very time I shout her, she is in a rush

L ater, when she's at the park, birds are singing and the trees are swinging

L isten to her yawn and stretch

A fter that, we fly back home.

Ada Airey (7)

Little Heaton CE Primary School, Rhodes, Middleton

The Powl King

My powl king is sassy, slimy, cute,
His name is Tiny Tim,
He is mixed with an owl and a penguin,
His favourite food is chicken wings,
He always loves to sing,
He always acts like a sassy king,
One day, he got a ring.

Derek Boyd (9)
Little Heaton CE Primary School, Rhodes, Middleton

The Liocat

L azy, lazy liocat!

I love you!

O range, yellow, black and pink

C ome on, small and cute liocat

A gentle and wild liocat

T he liocat to the rescue!

Evelynn Jennings (9)

Little Heaton CE Primary School, Rhodes, Middleton

My Majestic Hamster

The minute I set my eyes on her,
I felt like I could do a million backflips!
I fluttered with joy!
When I come back from school,
My heart rejoices!
When I'm stressed, I come to you,
Even when I'm doing a poo!
You are the apple of my eye,
When you climb the cage,
I feel like I can pass out from your cuteness!
Your positivity is infectious!
Flowers will die, the sun will set,
But you're a hamster I'll never forget!
Your name is so precious, it will never grow old,
It's engraved in my heart in letters and gold.

Amber Suttie (10)
North Beckton Primary School, Beckton

Flames Up, Up And Away!

Flames the dragon,
Has a flagon,
In his wagon,
When he takes it out,
He always wanders about,
When Flames is lost,
His brain's been tossed,
When he is away flying,
He likes to start spying

Anujan Nirubaraj (9)

Sacred Heart Primary School, Battersea

The Scary Wolf

N ight comes and Night Hunter comes out
I ts black coat is as dark as space
G rowling through the darkness looking for prey
H e finds his prey and eats it whole
T he day comes and he goes to his cave

H is howl makes his fur turn to acid
U nhappy with his prey, he sets out to hunt bigger animals
N ext, he had to fight a giant king cobra
T hen he bit the wolf in the paw
E ventually, the wolf scarred the king cobra's eye
R *oar!* The wolf won the battle by cutting the king cobra's head.

Igor Luc (9)
St David's Primary School, Plains

Soapy The Cat

I have a cat called Soapy,
I adopted her from the shop.
There were millions of cats,
There may be even more!
But when I saw Soapy,
I thought she was unique.
She had blue eyes,
Like no other black cats had.
She had a pool of water,
That she loved and chilled in.
I dashed up to the counter,
My hair shining in the light.
I bought Soapy and took her home.
Straight away I gave her a pool of water
And she popped all the bubbles.
There's no other pet like her.
She's the best!

Nicole Paterson (9)
St David's Primary School, Plains

The Rare Cobraconda

C obraconda is the rarest pet ever
O verall, he is more kind than frightening
B ut he is still dangerous
R oar! That's what he does when he is hungry
A lthough he is scary, he is actually friendly
C obraconda is a mix between a cobra and a green anaconda
O n Wednesdays, he gets a crocodile for dinner
N ight fell and Cobraconda went hunting
D estroying mountains with his plasma blast
A ll the snakes bow to him.

Aaron McDonald (8)
St David's Primary School, Plains

Karate Kit

Karate Kit is a black cat,
He loves to fight,
He can get you down on the ground,
In one slash!
He loves vegetables,
And he is a bit different to most cats.
Once he crept up on a robber,
Slish, slash! He was on the ground.
Kit loves to do karate,
And he is actually a black belt.
He saw a dog and...
Slish, slash!
The dog was away in no time.
He doesn't need weapons to defend himself,
All he needs are his fists.

Erin Hughes (9)
St David's Primary School, Plains

Talented Timmy

One day, when I was going to the park,
I noticed a creature in the bush.

I went over to check, then... *whoosh!*
Something white dashed out of the bush!
A rabbit, I thought.

It did flips and tricks,
Headstands, handstands and more!

All of a sudden, it jumped in the air,
And vanished forever.

Joseph Docherty (9)
St David's Primary School, Plains

The Multi-Talented Dog - Dainty Daisy

Dainty Daisy was no other normal dog,
She was a dog that had special superpowers,
She could fly high in the sky,
And shoot lasers out of her paws,
She could also run as fast as lightning,
She was the strongest dog in the world,
She was a really cool, multi-talented dog,
Unlike other dogs, she was multi-talented.

Harris Rodgers (9)
St David's Primary School, Plains

The Special Kitsune

K icking Kitsune is so special
I t lives in my massive bedroom closet
T he Kitsune is tiny
S ometimes it can fly and go colourful
U sually eats apples because it's his favourite food
N ever growls or bites anyone
E xtra sleeps at night so it has super vision.

Kaylee White (9)
St David's Primary School, Plains

Lucy The Rock Star Fennec Fox

Running wild with her bushy tail,
Big ears and a great sense of smell,
Watching the sunrise in a place called home,
Where the Sahara pyramids roam,
Lucy the fennec having a ball,
Searching for her new-found treat;
Spiders, snakes and all things smelly,
Lucy the rock star is a messy little lady.

Reece Rogerson (9)
St David's Primary School, Plains

Spot The Dog

Spot was a hero,
Oh, everybody loved him,
Tiny Spot the dog couldn't die!
Did you know that Spot the dog,
Could be a bit dangerous,
Over the clouds he flies,
Good Spot the dog,
Saving the day all the time.

Conlan Lane (9)
St David's Primary School, Plains

The Secret Life Of Fish

When I come out of my room,
The fish say, "She's gonna leave soon."
They look at the sun to have more fun,
A cat jumps in,
And bites off his fin,
It ends really bad,
All the fish are sad,
At least he's not dead,
Like Romeo and Juliet,
He'll have to go to bed,
He's turned all red,
His fin grows back,
They put flowers in a sack,
The fish priest comes and blesses him,
And tells him not to ever sin,
I come back and snap, it's back to normal,
But still, we have no coral.

Ilona Dabal (9)
St Mary's Catholic Primary School, Newcastle-Under-Lyme

Ollie The Dog's Fun House!

Ollie the dog was a fun little hog,
He jumped about doing tricks,
The others thought he would get sick,
Running around all day,
Which is the one you have to pay,
He loves telling us all jokes,
The crowd thought he was just broke,
All the love that he needed,
Which was the thing he succeeded,
All the stuff that he made,
Others would just play the games,
All it needed was a joke,
And *boom!* He was the opposite of broke!

Ollie the dog is a fun little hog!
Would you agree?

Brandon Lewis (9)
St Mary's Catholic Primary School, Newcastle-Under-Lyme

The Amazing Parrots

My dad got some pets
He told me to go to the vets
I told him it was nearly night
He told me I was right
He said he will take the tag
And he told me not to nag
My parrots like to bite
And they will fly like a flight
My dad already is done
So he told me to have fun
The birds went to fly
So he went to wave them bye!

Crash! The birds went through the glass!

Vismaya Suresh (9)
St Mary's Catholic Primary School, Newcastle-Under-Lyme

About My Dog

B est friends, me and my dog are best friends

U s, me and my dog are both lazy

S illy because every time he plays with his ball, it always gets stuck under the sofa

T ime, every time I say, "Time for walkies." He goes crazy.

E at, every time he does this, he gets more food on the floor instead of his mouth

R ode, one time he was asleep on a skateboard.

Cobi Greenhalgh (10)
St Mary's Catholic Primary School, Newcastle-Under-Lyme

Scally The Exquisite

S cally is an amazing, exquisite, obedient dinosaur

C arefully pet him because of his dangerous spikes

A ll of Scally's friends are just like Scally

L ots of Scally's scales are green but hairy

L oads of his dino buddies have sleepovers but mostly with Scally

Y ou can be friends with him only if you visit the zoo.

Jayden Laidlaw (9)

St Mary's Catholic Primary School, Newcastle-Under-Lyme

Homework Cat

My cute cat is a girl
But she dances and twirls
My cat's fingers are tiny
But her blue eyes are very shiny
She is very cute
But she eats a lot of healthy fruit
She is very clever
But she is my best friend ever
She is very small
She plays with a ball
She is very gentle
But she checks her teeth to the dental.

Jathurika Thineswaran (9)
St Mary's Catholic Primary School, Newcastle-Under-Lyme

My Pet Blizzard

B lizzard is my cute cat
L ater on, she's in my hat
I love stroking her soft fur
Z ap! She's here, she loves me and I love her
Z zzz! She's sleeping in her bed
A fter, she's by my head
R eally soft, really, really soft
D inner time, come out the loft.

Phoenix Tomlinson (9)
St Mary's Catholic Primary School, Newcastle-Under-Lyme

Kaylin The Cat

K aylin the beautiful cat, it's one special cat

A cat that's running and loves to cuddle

Y awning, so cute, opens one eye to see if I'm there

L ittle but cute, she jumps on me, wants food

I n the morning, takes a wee

N ow that's the end of our poem.

Noel Jomon (9)
St Mary's Catholic Primary School, Newcastle-Under-Lyme

The Barn Of Animals

Cows mooing and shouting, "Food!"
Chickens angry, they're in a bad mood!
Pigs rolling and jumping into mud,
Bulls ready to practise against wood,
Birds yelling in the yard,
All the animals in a barn.

Bang! The barn doors close!

Marcus Otter (10)
St Mary's Catholic Primary School, Newcastle-Under-Lyme

My Fish

One day, I remembered about my old frogs,
So I asked my mum for fish,
But she said, "No and no and no."
But I kept asking and she said, "No."
And one day, she said maybe.
I was super happy.
The next day, I woke up with my fish.

Jake Huxley (9)
St Mary's Catholic Primary School, Newcastle-Under-Lyme

About My Go Dog

My dog is called Daisy,
She is so lazy,
When I come down,
All I hear is *snore, snore, snore* till 10 am.
When we do a race,
She always wins.
She sees a bird, *runnnn!*
I'm on the chase!

Archie Bailey (9)
St Mary's Catholic Primary School, Newcastle-Under-Lyme

My Dog Poppy

P olar bears are cute like Poppy
O ops, she got the bin out
P *op!* Poppy's scared of loud things
P oppy plays for a bit
Y awn, goodnight Poppy.

Millie Barker (9)

St Mary's Catholic Primary School, Newcastle-Under-Lyme

Monty And Me

Me and Monty are the best of friends
When he eats all the hens
We aren't really,
Then he got hit by a car,
But that could not stop him,
My cat is strong,
My Monty and me.

Myles Rogers (9)
St Mary's Catholic Primary School, Newcastle-Under-Lyme

Superhero Pet

S uper
U p in the sky
P ast the clouds
E ast is the way
R eady to fly in the sky.

Sulaiman Alam (9)
St Mary's Catholic Primary School, Newcastle-Under-Lyme

Tim, My Inventing Tortoise

There was once an inventing tortoise,
I called him Doctor Tim,
And before he had his adventure,
His life was rather dim.

Doctor Tim was a slow coach,
Who dreamed of going fast,
So he got to work inventing,
And put behind his past.

Then Tim did some drilling,
And then he used the saw,
He stopped for some juicy lettuce,
Then decided to drill some more.

And there it was, the Turbo-Tortoiser,
Gleaming, sparkling and new,
As he gazed into his invention,
His tortoisey smile grew.

He sold his gadgets for millions,
He was as rich as rich could be,

He could buy whatever he dreamed of,
Like a yacht to sail the sea.

The Turbo-Tortoiser was simple,
With it, you wouldn't go slow,
There were four rocket-powered boots,
So you could zoom where you wanted to go.

Speed limits were broken!
My pet was worshipped over the land,
And in Southern Northern America,
There was an 'I love Doctor Tim' stand.

And then came that fateful night,
Disaster struck. *Kaboom!*
Tim's control computer exploded,
And sparks flew up to the moon!

And as Tim opened the window,
His face fell into a frown,
Instead of seeing mates speed to work,
There were just empty fields of brown.

Then he picked up his tortoise phone,
And he read the fateful news,

He slowly trudged over to the door,
And sadly put on four tiny shoes.

You see the Turbo-Tortoisers,
Had defaulted and tripled their power,
Why, when it all seemed so perfect,
Did something have to go so sour?

So my poor Tim lost all his money,
And went back to liking slow,
But then he had another idea,
To make him as slow as slow could go...

Elizabeth Lees (11)
St Thomas' CE Primary School, Stockton Heath

Hero Hamster

In the day, he's as small as a bee,
In the night, he's as tall as a tree,
While you're away,
He will save the day,
His name is Robin.

Monsters and creatures giving you a fright,
They're being destructive throughout the night,
But Robin my hamster isn't scared,
So if I were you, monsters, I would be prepared,
With his mighty wings, he can defeat anything.

I wouldn't blink,
He's quicker than you think,
He is my gorgeous pet Robin.

Amy Smith (10)
St Thomas' CE Primary School, Stockton Heath

The Sassy Snail

Deep in the woodland trees,
where nobody ever sees,
buzz the old, grumpy bumblebees.
The mischievous ants that steal leaves,
and a sassy snail called Louise.

Now here's the thing about Louise,
she is sassy, she never says thank you or even
please.
And deep down in those woodland trees,
she has no friends to play with at ease.

One morning, Louise woke up in her grand house
of leaves,
to a cool and very chilly breeze.
Today she had some jobs to do,
her birthday party invitations were due.

She strutted down to her neighbour's fort,
her first invitation was going to the marvellous
monkey - Mark Short.
"Oi, you fluffball in the trees, what are you doing
later?"

"I'm hanging out with my friend Amy the alligator,"
said Mark the monkey,
"Well, you and your sharp-toothed friend are
invited to my brilliant birthday party."
And with that, Louise was out.

As she walked up to Jeff the giraffe in his long and
very tall tree house,
she stumbled upon a small and timid mouse,
"I, I, I heard you were having a party at your grand
leaf house," the mouse spluttered,
"So what?" Louise shouted.
The mouse scuttered,
she walked up to Jeff's tree,
and rubbed her hands with glee.

Within an hour, she had invited the whole village,
and she had this image,
of a perfect night,
but when it came round,
she had a fright.
There was not a sound,
as nobody had come,
she felt so sad and really glum.

She had been so mean,
no one was on her team.

So that is why you should always be nice to other people.

Ava Rutter (10)
St Thomas' CE Primary School, Stockton Heath

Jeff The Phenomenon

J eff - half fox, half giraffe...

E vil and devious; cunning and sly - always up for a laugh

F urry skin in tones of red, orange and reddish-purple

F erocious and yet strangely adorable

G eroxes are very dangerous

E very little part of their body is always awake

R are to come by...

O r you're just really, really unlucky

X ylophone provides a lullaby for sleep.

Daniel Bruford (10)
St Thomas' CE Primary School, Stockton Heath

Dusty The Turbo Cat!

A pink, fluffy cat
Running in a field
Catching mice and voles
She dances around
Keeping her territory safe
With her pink fur
And black button nose.

As fast as a bullet
She dodges the dogs
Past the birds, the trees
And the mice
On her way home
With her pink fur
And black button nose.

Eating her munchies
She thinks of the days
When she could run free
Having fun all the way
With her pink fur
And black button nose.

Sleeping soundly at night
She dreams of all the mice
She could catch
In the grassy fields
For her name is Dusty
With her pink fur
And black button nose.

Phoebe Roberts (10)
St Thomas' CE Primary School, Stockton Heath

Hugo

Naughty, cute and messy, Hugo is,
He'll rip your skin to make marks on it,
I want him in my life, even though he's like that,
When he's on a walk, he's adorable and friendly,
He can be dirty if he runs in a puddle,
But oh, he absolutely hates bath time,
When he runs, Hugo bounces like a bunny,
Hugo can make you angry,
Like the time he ate my homework,
I'll always love Hugo, no matter what.

Kitty Rose Richards (11)
St Thomas' CE Primary School, Stockton Heath

Diva Kitten Strikes Again!

Diva Kitten,
You did it again,
You have little mittens,
That we just can't resist,
I just don't get it!
Why they like this plain act of yours,
Your claws are old and dirty,
Why, oh, just why,
You're just a cat with sunglasses,
Don't forget how you sing,
I don't get how that's special,
I think I get it now,
You're a mischievous kitten,
Already on your last life.

Chloe Porter (10)
St Thomas' CE Primary School, Stockton Heath

The Grumpy Guinea Pig

A grumpy little guinea pig,
Sits in his cage all day,
And although his belly is rather big,
"I love you lots," is all I ever say.

His gleaming little eyes,
And his crinkled little nose,
Stare up at the blue skies,
But his grumpy face still shows.

He wears a little frown,
And a massive furry coat,
It's like he runs his own town,
Where no one but he may gloat.

Millie Garner (10)
St Thomas' CE Primary School, Stockton Heath

Bill And Ted

Bill and Ted are really well fed,
Almost every night they sleep in Mum's bed.
Sometimes they bring a mouse,
Into our four-storey house.
Ted is lazy, Bill is not,
Bill goes out and Ted often sleeps a lot.
Sometimes we even make the cats,
Wear tiny bobble hats!
I love my cats!

George Lawton (10)
St Thomas' CE Primary School, Stockton Heath

A Fluffy Tortoise

My tortoise is fun and fluffy,
But she can be so lazy,
And sleeps all day long.
Her favourite food is usually clover,
Her incredible, fluffy fur on her shell,
Keeps her warm in the winter.

Willow Taw (7)
Swaffham Prior CE Primary School, Swaffham Prior

Pets

P ets are peculiar, just like mine
E very day they make a rhyme
T elling people how weird you are
S oon you'll get a pet's guitar.

Luciana Verlander (8)
Swaffham Prior CE Primary School, Swaffham Prior

My Peculiar Pet!

A kennings poem

Ball catcher
Dribble master
Furry howler
Pyjama lover
Good retriever
Very naughty
Sleep hater

It's a dog.

Daisy Jarvis Bently (8)
Swaffham Prior CE Primary School, Swaffham Prior

Goat-A-Claus

When we're asleep dreaming,
He comes down the chimney,
Assuming he's going to get soot in his sack,
That's a fact,
Now let me tell you more...
He's nice, he likes rice,
Likes a good price at Asda,
But all of them things,
Mean one thing.
On the 25th of December,
Watch out!
He might be about,
If you've been good.
So be careful,
Goat-A-Claus is here...

Kane Ryan Barlow (10)
The Orchard School, Canterbury

Colourful Cat

R osie is her name
A nd she is the most colourful cat
I dress her in cute outfits
N ow, what do you think of that?
B ows of colour in-between her tiny ears
O h, how adorably soft and cuddly
W e'll be together for years.

Phoebe Nicol (9)

Watlington Community Primary School, Watlington

Elsa Elephant

Elsa Elephant is my new pet,
She was the first talking animal I'd ever met!

She's so unusual, she breathes out water and fire,
It's so cool, my friends even call me a liar!

She looks so small in the house,
She's almost a tiny mouse!

Elsa Elephant helps to fire fight,
She squirts all the flames in her sight.

I love my white elephant with her sparkly eyes,
Honestly, I don't mind her little size!

Amélie Russell (10)
Wemms Education Centre, Leatherhead

YOUNG wRITERS INFORMATION

We hope you have enjoyed reading this book – and that you will continue to in the coming years.

If you're a young writer who enjoys reading and creative writing, or the parent of an enthusiastic poet or story writer, do visit our website **www.youngwriters.co.uk**. Here you will find free competitions, workshops and games, as well as recommended reads, a poetry glossary and our blog. There's lots to keep budding writers motivated to write!

If you would like to order further copies of this book, or any of our other titles, then please give us a call or order via your online account.

Young Writers
Remus House
Coltsfoot Drive
Peterborough
PE2 9BF
(01733) 890066
info@youngwriters.co.uk

Join in the conversation!
Tips, news, giveaways and much more!

 YoungWritersUK    @YoungWritersCW